TRACTOR TOM AND THE MOBILE PHONE

by Mark Holloway

First published 2003 by Contender Books
Contender Books is a division of
The Contender Entertainment Group
48 Margaret Street
London W1W 8SE
www.contendergroup.com/books

**For more Tractor Tom fun and games, log on to his website
http://www.tractortom.com**

This edition published 2003
1 3 5 7 9 10 8 6 4 2

© 1989 Great Ormond Street Hospital Children's Charity.
Registered charity no. 235825.
The Contender Entertainment Group will give 5p from the sale of this
Tractor Tom product to Great Ormond Street Hospital Children's Charity.

ISBN 1 84357 064 5

Designed by BURVILLE RILEY
Printed in Italy

THIS BOOK BELONGS TO
TRACTOR TOM'S FRIEND

....

It's another busy day at Springhill Farm. Matt wants to show Fi his brand new mobile phone.

Oh no! – he's lost it.
"Tom-tom! Tom-tom! Tom-tom!"
Who's that? Hurray! It's Tractor Tom!
He'll soon find Matt's phone.

Farmer Fi has a good idea. If she calls Matt's telephone number, Matt's phone will ring. Then all Tom has to do is listen carefully, and the ringing noise will tell him exactly where the phone is.

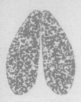
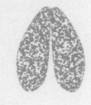

"Moo-moo! Moo-moo! Moo-moo!"
Is that Matt's mobile phone ringing?
No, it's Mo the cow!

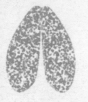

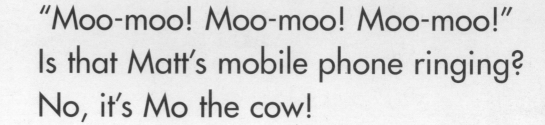

"Baa-baa! Baa-baa! Baa-baa!"
Is that Matt's mobile phone ringing?
No, it's the sheep.

"Wheezy-wheezy! Wheezy-wheezy! Wheezy-wheezy!"
Is that Matt's mobile phone ringing?
No, it's Wheezy the combine harvester. He's fast asleep and he's snoring very loudly.

"Quack-quack! Quack-quack! Quack-quack!"

Is that Matt's mobile phone ringing? No, it's those cheeky ducks, Wack and Bach. But what are they playing with?

Tom knows just what to do.
He wakes up Purdey the cat and
helps her to chase the naughty
ducks away.

Wack and Bach are so surprised they jump up and race off as fast as they can. Look! They've left Matt's phone in Rev!

"Ring-ring! Ring-ring! Ring-ring!"
Matt picks up his phone.
"Hello, Fi. Tom's found my phone,"
says Matt. "What would we do
without him?"

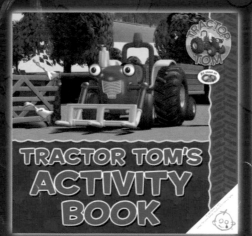
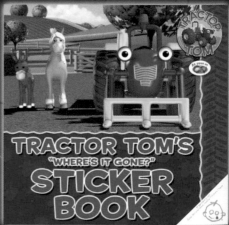